Grade Five

Classical Guitar Playing

Compiled and edited by
Tony Skinner and Raymond Burley

Printed and bound in Great Britain

Published by Registry Publications

Registry Mews, 11-13 Wilton Rd, Bexhill, Sussex, TN40 1HY

Cover guitars: Rohan Lowe, John Price, Martin Fleeson

A CIP record for this publication is available from the British Library
ISBN: 1-898466-65-3

Compiled for **LCM Examinations** by

www.RegistryOfGuitarTutors.com

INTRODUCTION

This publication is part of a progressive series of ten handbooks, primarily intended for candidates considering taking the London College Of Music examinations in classical guitar playing. However, given each handbook's wide content of musical repertoire, and associated educational material, the series provides a solid foundation of musical education for any classical guitar student – whether intending to take an examination or not. Whilst the handbooks can be used for independent study, they are ideally intended as a supplement to individual or group tuition.

Examination entry

An examination entry form is provided at the rear of each handbook. This is the only valid entry form for the London College Of Music classical guitar examinations. Please note that *if the entry form is detached and lost, it will not be replaced under any circumstances* and the candidate will be required to obtain a replacement handbook to obtain another entry form.

Editorial information

All performance pieces should be played in full, including all repeats shown. The pieces have been edited specifically for examination use, with all non-required repeat markings omitted. Examination performances must be from this handbook edition. Tempos, fingering, and dynamic markings are for general guidance only and need not be rigidly adhered to. In some pieces such markings are kept to a minimum to allow candidates to display individual interpretation; the omission of editorial dynamic markings does not in any way imply that dynamic variation should be absent from a performance.

Right-hand fingering is normally shown on the stem side of the notes:
p = thumb; *i* = index; *m* = middle; *a* = third.

Left-hand fingering is shown with the numbers **1 2 3 4**, normally to the left side of the note head. **0** indicates an open string.

String numbers are shown in a circle, normally below the note. For example, ⑥ = 6th string.

Finger shifts are indicated by a small horizontal dash before the left hand finger number. For example, **2** followed by **-2** indicates that the 2nd finger can stay on the same string but move to another fret as a *guide finger*. The finger shift sign should not be confused with a *slide* or *glissando* (where a longer dash joins two noteheads).

Slurs are indicated by a curved line between two or more notes of differing pitch. These should not be confused with *ties* (where notes of the *same* pitch are joined by a curved line).

Full barrés (covering 5 or 6 strings with the first finger) are shown by a capital **B**, followed by a Roman numeral to indicate the fret position of the barré. For example, **BV** indicates a full barré at the fifth fret. A dotted line will indicate the duration for which the barré should be held. *Half barrés* (covering 2 to 4 strings) are shown like this: **½B**, followed by a Roman numeral to indicate the fret position of the half barré.

Harmonics are shown with a diamond-shaped notehead. The fret at which they should be played is shown above each note, e.g. **H12** for the 12th fret, and the string number will be shown. On the stave, harmonics are placed at the pitch of the fretted note above which they are played – rather than the pitch at which they sound.

Arpeggiated chords, that are strummed or rolled, are indicated by a vertical wavy line to the left of the chord.

Acknowledgements

The editors acknowledge the help of the many libraries and copyright owners that facilitated access to original manuscripts, source materials and facsimiles. The editors are grateful for the advice and support of all the members of the Registry Of Guitar Tutors 'Classical Guitar Advisory Panel', and are particularly indebted for the expertise and contributions of:

Carlos Bonell Hon.RCM, Chris Ackland GRSM LRAM LTCL,
Chaz Hart LRAM, Frank Bliven BM MA, Alan J. Brown LTCL.

SECTION ONE – FINGERBOARD KNOWLEDGE

The examiner may ask you to play *from memory* any of the scales, arpeggios or chords shown on the following pages. Note that major scales may be requested in *any* key. The major scale patterns shown overleaf are 'transpositional', i.e. they can be transposed to other keys by using the same finger pattern starting from a different fret.

Scales and arpeggios must be played *ascending and descending*, i.e. from the lowest note to the highest and back again, without a pause and without repeating the top note. It is recommended that arpeggios and double-stopped scales are played *tirando* (i.e. using free strokes), and that all other scales are played *apoyando* (i.e. using rest strokes). However, either method can be used providing a good tone is produced. Any effective and systematic combination of alternating fingers may be used to pick the strings.

Chords should be played *ascending only*, and sounded string by string, starting with the lowest root note. To achieve a legato sound, the whole chord shape should be placed on the fingerboard before, and kept on during, playing. Chords should always be played *tirando,* i.e. using free strokes. The following right-hand fingering is recommended for chords: *p* for all bass strings, *ima* for the treble strings.

To allow for flexibility in teaching and playing approaches, all the fingering suggestions within this handbook are *not* compulsory and alternative systematic fingerings, that are musically effective, will be accepted. Suggested tempos are for general guidance only. Slightly slower or faster performances will be acceptable, providing that the tempo is maintained evenly throughout. Overall, the examiner will be listening, and awarding marks, for accuracy, evenness and clarity.

A maximum of 15 marks may be awarded in this section of the examination.

Recommended tempo

Scales: 116 minim beats per minute	Double-stopped scales: 58 minim beats per minute
Arpeggios: 88 minim beats per minute	Chords: 132 minim beats per minute

---

Key Study

The Key Study links the introduction of a new key to the performance of a short melodic theme from a piece by a well-known composer. The purpose is to make the learning of scales relevant to practical music-making and therefore memorable, as well as providing the opportunity to play music outside the standard guitar repertoire.

The examiner may request you to play any, or all, of the scales within the key study. The examiner will also ask for a performance of ONE of the melodic themes of your choice.

Tempo markings and fingering are for guidance only and need not be rigidly adhered to, providing a good musical performance is produced. The examiner will be listening, and awarding marks, for evidence of melodic phrasing and shaping, as well as for accuracy and clarity.

The Key Study must be played entirely from memory.

C Major scale - 2 octaves (Transpositional pattern)

To play this scale in the key of Db Major, begin with the 2nd finger on the 4th fret of the 5th string. Use this pattern to play D Major (5th fret), Eb Major (6th fret), E Major (7th fret), F Major (8th fret) and F# Major (9th fret)

G Major scale - 2 octaves (Transpositional pattern)

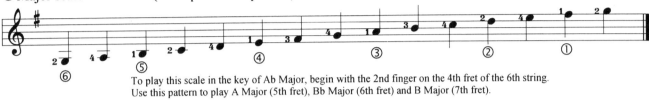

To play this scale in the key of Ab Major, begin with the 2nd finger on the 4th fret of the 6th string. Use this pattern to play A Major (5th fret), Bb Major (6th fret) and B Major (7th fret).

E Chromatic scale - 3 octaves

E Major scale - 3 octaves

E Harmonic Minor scale - 3 octaves

E Melodic Minor scale - 3 octaves

E Major scale in 3rds - 1 octave

E Major scale in 10ths - 1 octave

E Major arpeggio - 3 octaves

E Minor arpeggio - 3 octaves

E Dominant 7th arpeggio - 3 octaves

Ab Major Barré chord

Eb Major Barré chord

F Minor Barré chord

C Minor Barré chord

Key Study

The examiner will request a selection of the scales below,
plus ONE melodic theme of the *candidate's choice.*

Ab Major scale - 2 octaves

F Harmonic Minor scale - 2 octaves

F Melodic Minor scale - 2 octaves

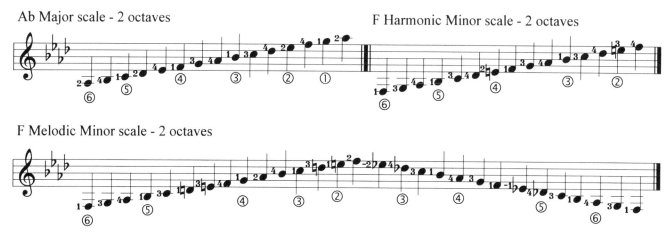

Melodic theme - Option One

Serenade

Franz Joseph Haydn
(1732 - 1809)

Melodic theme - Option Two

La Donna E Mobile
From Rigoletto

Giuseppe Verdi
(1813 - 1901)

SECTION TWO – PERFORMANCE

Candidates should play *one* piece from each of the three groups. A maximum of 60 marks may be awarded in this section of the examination – i.e. up to 20 marks for each performance.

Fingering and tempo markings are for general guidance only and do not need to be adhered to strictly, however all repeat markings should be followed. The performance notes below are intended to provide helpful advice and information, however candidates are free to present alternative technical solutions and musical interpretations – providing that a musically effective and stylistically appropriate result is achieved.

PERFORMANCE NOTES

My Lord Willoughby's Welcome Home *(Dowland)*:

This piece was originally written for the lute by John Dowland – perhaps the most renowned lutenist of all time. Dowland lived in England, but travelled widely in Europe and was even appointed as lutenist to the King of Denmark. This piece should be played with a light touch to ensure a sense of movement, particularly during the last eight bars. In bar 3, sustain the semibreve F for its full value. In bars 14 and 15 ensure that all three voices are clearly defined.

Prelude *(Visée)*:

This piece was originally written for the baroque guitar by French guitarist Robert de Visée. Held in high esteem as a guitarist, Visée was employed as a musician in the French royal court and as guitar teacher to Louis XIV. This piece formed part of Visée's Suite in D minor. In French performance style of the period the piece would have been played with 'unequal rhythm', but this is not expected at this grade. The use of slurs in bars 8 and 9 will help smooth the playing of the fast semiquaver runs.

Preludio, O Capricho Arpeado *(Sanz)*:

This piece is taken from the composer's treatise *Instruccion de Musica Sobre la Guitarra Espanola* reprinted finally in 1697. It was written for the five course (baroque) guitar. Dynamics are absent from the tablature of the original edition, and have been deliberately omitted from this edition. However, the piece will benefit considerably from some dynamic shaping, and this has been left to the performer's discretion. Although there should be a change in rhythmic emphasis with the changes in time signature in bars 8 and 15, there should be no interruption to the flow of the music and no change of tempo.

Andantino *(Carcassi)*:

Born in Italy, Matteo Carcassi later made France his home. As a virtuoso performer on the guitar, Carcassi regularly toured Europe. He wrote much music for the guitar, including many studies and a successful guitar teaching method. This piece forms part of his popular collection *25 Melodic and Progressive Studies Opus 60*. Wherever possible, the notes within each bar should be held on to form chord shapes. The notes with upward stems, mainly lying on the 1st and 2nd strings, should be sounded clearly – via the use of rest strokes, if so desired. Use of rubato in places would enhance the performance.

Romance *(Anon.)*:

This popular Spanish melody is in two distinct sections; the first in E minor, the second in E major. The melody, which is almost entirely on the first string, should be played with a full and sonorous tone, which may be enhanced with the use of vibrato. The triplet accompaniment should not be over emphasised or allowed to distract attention from the melody. The second section involves some wide stretches that require careful and gradual preparation.

Lágrima *(Tárrega)*:

Spanish guitarist Francisco Tárrega is often called 'the father of the modern classical guitar' due to his great influence on expanding its technique and repertoire. This piece is in two distinct eight bar sections: the first in E major, the second in E minor. There is much fingerboard movement and due attention should be given to left-hand fingering. The title indicates that a *tearful* mood should be portrayed in the performance style. The melody, which is mainly on the first string, should be well-defined with a full, but not overpowering, tone.

Prelude *(Benham)*:

One distinctive feature of this piece, by the British guitarist and educator Patrick Benham, is the use of overlapping notes to give a harp-like effect. The piece requires the 6th string to be tuned down to D: all notes on the 6th string will be two frets higher with this tuning. If you are not used to this tuning, practise de-tuning and re-tuning changing in order to avoid any problems during the examination. The composer advises that performers should: "avoid a mechanical beat and try to establish a warm, flowing effect assisted by the occasional use of vibrato".

Reflections No.2 *(Skinner)*:

This piece, by the British music educator and composer Tony Skinner, is from his suite *Reflections – Five Pieces For Guitar*. The tempo for the opening 13 bars should not be strict, and there is much room for the use of carefully considered rubato in order to capture the *misterioso* mood of this section. Notes should be held on to form chord shapes wherever possible. This applies throughout the piece, but particularly in bars 14 to 21. From bar 22 onwards, the 1st string melody notes (shown with upward stems) should be sounded strongly and clearly, but without the use of rest strokes.

Fields Of Green *(Smith)*:

This is the opening piece from British guitarist/composer Jasper Smith's *Five Pictures Of Norfolk*. The composer states that: "*Fields Of Green* has a gentle pastoral style and an even relaxed feel should be maintained. The full barrés in measures 5 and 6, whilst not essential, will help facilitate a smooth chord change. Observing the fingering carefully in bars 31 to 33 will avoid awkward jumps with the left hand. The use of ligado where marked should aid the flow of the piece."

My Lord Willoughby's Welcome Home

[Group A]

John Dowland
(1563 - 1626)

10

Prélude

Robert de Visée
(1660 - 1720)

[Group A]

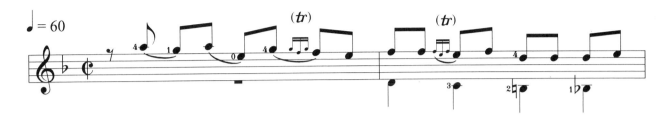

11

Preludio, O Capricho Arpeado

[Group A]

Gaspar Sanz
(c.1640 - c.1710)

12

Andantino Op.60 No.3

[Group B]

Matteo Carcassi
(1792 - 1853)

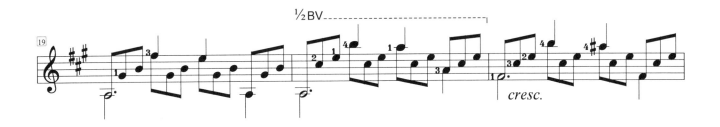

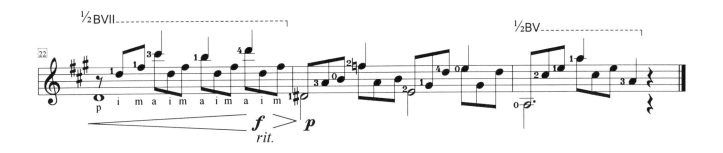

Romance

[Group B]

Anon.
(Trad. 19th Century)

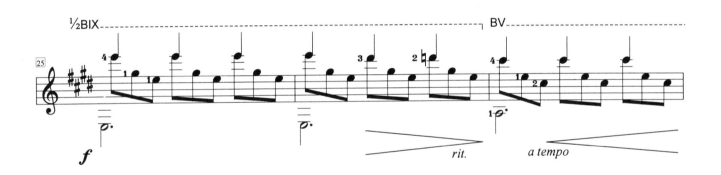

Lágrima

[Group B]

Francisco Tárrega
(1852 - 1909)

Prelude

[Group C]

Patrick Benham
(1940 -)

19

Reflections No.2

[Group C]

Tony Skinner
(1960 -)

20

Fields Of Green

[Group C]

Jasper Smith
(1966 -)

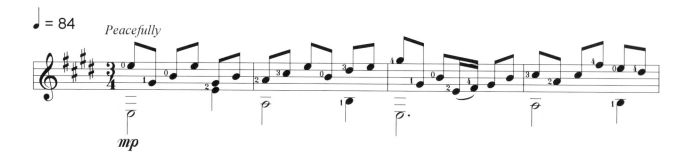

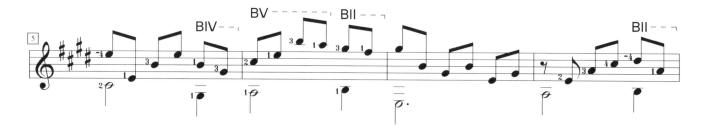

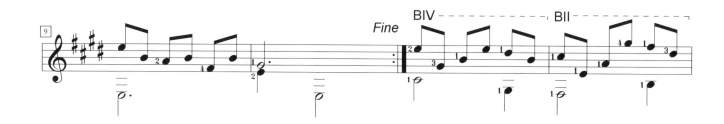

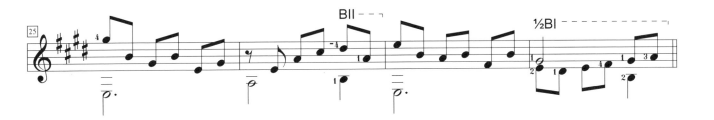

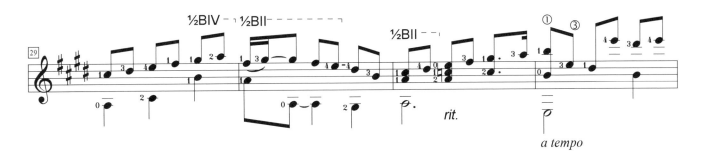

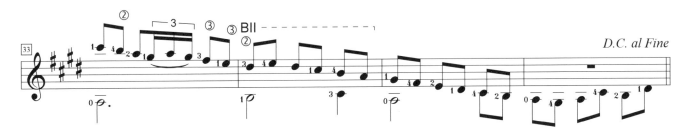

SECTION THREE – MUSICAL KNOWLEDGE

A maximum of 7 marks may be awarded in this section of the examination. The examiner will ask questions, mainly based on the music performed, to test the candidate's understanding of any obvious formal structures and melodic and harmonic features of the music. The examiner will also test for an understanding of the rudiments of music to a level appropriate to the grade – including knowledge of any terms and signs that appear in the music performed. In addition, an outline knowledge of the composers and style of the pieces performed will be expected. Some useful information in this respect will be found in the *Performance Notes* in the previous chapter. Candidates should also refer to the Introduction of this handbook which outlines the meaning of specialist guitar signs and symbols.

Potential candidates lacking knowledge in this general area are advised to study for the LCM Theory of Music examinations, using suitable music theory books, worksheets and musical dictionaries. Some reference to relevant musical history books and composer biographies would also be helpful. Advice and tuition from an experienced teacher would undoubtedly prove most advantageous. It is also recommended that candidates attend concerts, and listen to a broad range of recordings of the composer's works, to gain insights into performance and style.

The information below (based on a selection of the pieces) provides a general guideline to, and some examples of, the *type* of questions that may be asked at this grade. The list is neither exclusive nor exhaustive.

My Lord Willoughby's Welcome Home (Dowland)
Q: Can you identify the chord in bar 8?
A: It is an E major chord.

Q: What key does the piece modulate to and remain in throughout bars 9 to 12?
A: G major

Q: What is the interval between the last two notes in bar 12?
A: A perfect fourth.

Q: What can you tell me about John Dowland and his music?
A: John Dowland was a renowned lutenist and successful songwriter. One of his most famous works is *Lachrimae Pavan*. He lived between 1563 and 1626 and was a contemporary of Monteverdi, Byrd and Cutting.

Prélude (Visée)
Q: What is a Prelude?
A: An instrumental piece that often precedes a fugue, or that forms the first part of a suite. This Prelude was the first movement in Robert de Visée's Suite in D minor.

Q: For which instrument was this piece originally written?
A: Baroque guitar.

Q: What can you tell me about Robert de Visée?
A: Visée lived approximately between 1660 and 1720. He was employed as a musician in the French royal court and as guitar teacher to Louis XIV. He composed numerous works for baroque guitar, most notably his well-known *Suite in D minor*.

Q: Can you identify the chord on the 3rd beat of bar 9?
A: The chord is A major.

Andantino (Carcassi)

Q: What is the *form* of this piece?

A: Binary

Q: Could you explain what that means in relation to this piece in a little more detail?

A: The *form* is the structure or framework of the lay-out of the music. *Binary Form* means that it is in two sections. In this piece, the A section begins in the key of A major and ends in E major (the dominant). The B section is longer and begins in the dominant, and eventually modulates back to the tonic key of A major.

Q: What does the number *3* that appears over groups of notes in bar 1 mean in practical terms?

A: It is a triplet and indicates that 3 notes should be played in the space of 2 notes of the same value.

Q: Can you name some other composers from broadly the same period as Carcassi?

A: Guitar composers from that time include Carulli and Sor; other well-known composers include Beethoven and Schubert.

Lágrima (Tárrega)

Q: What key is this piece in, and when does the key change?

A: The piece starts in E major and changes to E minor at bar 9 - which is the start of the *B* section.

Q: Identify any prominent melodic or harmonic feature of the piece.

A: The piece involves repeated use of major and minor 10th harmonised intervals, particularly at the start and throughout most of the *A* section, as well as in bar 13 of the *B* section.

Q: What chord occurs on the first beat of bar 12?

A: B major

Q: What does the marking *sotto voce* in bar 10 mean?

A: In an undertone, literally 'under the voice'.

Fields Of Green (Smith)

Q: Explain the meaning of the following terms that appear in the music:
   (a) rit. (b) a tempo.

A: (a) 'rit.' is short for 'ritenuto', meaning 'held back'; (b) resume normal speed after the deviation in tempo.

Q: Describe the structure of the piece.

A: Section A forms the main theme of the piece. This lasts for 10 bars, before being repeated. Section B, lasting 8 bars then follows, before section A is recalled with a variation in the final of its 10 bars. Section C, lasting 8 bars, then commences. The piece is completed by returning to Section A one final time.

Q: Can you expand a little more regarding the harmonic structure of the first section of this piece?

A: This is best analysed as five two-bar progressions, all based on arpeggiated chords. The key of the piece is E major. The first bar revolves around an E major chord, with the second bar comprising A major (the subdominant chord) and B major (the dominant). The next two bars are just a variation on the first two, as are bars 7 and 8. Bar 5 begins with the relative minor chord, whilst bar 6 is a variation on bar 2. The section closes with the tonic chord in bars 9 and 10. In several bars (such as bar 9) the harmony is made more interesting by the use of suspensions or extended notes, rather than solely chord tones.

Q: Can you supply any background information on this piece and its composer?

A: It was written by British born 20th century guitarist and composer Jasper Smith as part of his suite *Five Pictures Of Norfolk*.

SECTION FOUR – PLAYING AT SIGHT

The examiner will show you the sight reading test and allow you just a short time to look over it before asking you to perform it. A maximum of 10 marks may be awarded in this section of the examination. The table below shows the range of the piece:

Length	Keys	Time signatures	Note values	Fingerboard positions
8 bars	Major: F, C, G, D, A Minor: D, A, E, B, F#	2 3 4 6 4 4 4 8		1st / 2nd / 3rd

PERFORMANCE TIPS

1.   Always check the key and time signature BEFORE you start to play.

2.   Once you have identified the key it is helpful to remember that the notes will all come from the key scale.

3.   Quickly scan through the piece and check any chords or rhythms that you are unsure of. Where fretted bass notes occur simultaneously with melody notes, decide which left-hand fingering you will need to use.

4.   Note the tempo or style marking, but be careful not to play at a tempo at which you cannot maintain accuracy throughout.

5.   Once you start to play, try and keep your eyes on the music. Avoid the temptation to keep looking at the fingerboard – that's a sure way to lose your place in the music.

6.   Observe any rests and try to follow the dynamic markings.

7.   If you do make an error, try not to let it affect your confidence for the rest of the piece. It is better to keep going and capture the overall shape of the piece, rather than stopping or going back to correct errors.

The following examples show the *type* of pieces that will be presented in the examination.

i) Adagio

ii) Larghetto

iii) Moderato

iv) Andantino

27

SECTION FIVE – AURAL AWARENESS

A maximum of 8 marks may be awarded in this section of the examination. The tests will be played by the examiner on either guitar or piano, at the examiner's discretion. The examples below are shown in guitar notation and give a broad indication of the type of tests that will be given during the examination. Candidates wishing to view the piano notation for these tests should obtain the London College Of Music *Sample Ear Tests* booklet.

Rhythm tests

1. The examiner will play a short piece of music in simple or compound time, similar to the examples below. The candidate should beat time with a clear beat, in time with the examiner's playing. (The test may be played twice if necessary.) The compound test may be in two or six beats.

Example i.

Example ii.

Example iii.

Example iv.

2. The candidate should describe the rhythms in a two bar section of the same music. The section itself will be played once more, as a single line version. The excerpt below is taken from example iii above.

Pitch tests

1. The candidate should identify any major or minor interval within an octave by name and type, including the augmented fourth and diminished fifth, after the interval has been played by the examiner. The examiner may conduct this test twice, with two different intervals. Here is an example of the intervals in the key of C.

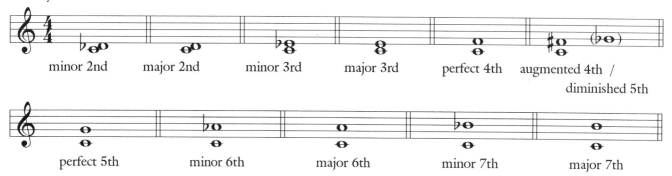

minor 2nd	major 2nd	minor 3rd	major 3rd	perfect 4th	augmented 4th /
					diminished 5th

perfect 5th   minor 6th   major 6th   minor 7th   major 7th

2. Identification of two cadences. Each cadence will be played as two chords at the end of a short melodic 'lead-in'. Each may be identified as "finished" (perfect or plagal) or "unfinished" (imperfect or interrupted) or by its conventional name. The tonic chord will be played at the start of each test.

London College of **Music** & **Media**
THAMES VALLEY UNIVERSITY

Examination Entry Form
for
Classical Guitar

GRADE FIVE
or Leisure Play Intermediate

PLEASE COMPLETE CLEARLY IN INK AND IN BLOCK CAPITAL LETTERS

SESSION (Spring/Summer/Winter): _____ YEAR: _____

Preferred Examination Centre (if known): _____
If left blank you will examined at the nearest venue to your home address.

Candidate Details:
Candidate Name (as to appear on certificate):

_____

Address: _____

_____ Postcode: _____

Tel. No. (day): _____ (evening): _____

Tick this box if you are also entering for LCM Theory of Music ☐
If so, which Grade? _____

Teacher Details:
Teacher Name (as to appear on certificate): _____

LCM Teacher Code (if entered previously): _____

RGT Tutor Code (if applicable): _____

Address: _____

_____ Postcode: _____

Tel. No. (day): _____ (evening): _____

Tick this box if any details above have changed since your last LCM entry ☐

Tick this box if the teacher has also entered pupils for ☐
RGT Electric or Bass Guitar examinations for the same session.

IMPORTANT NOTES

- It is the candidate's responsibility to have knowledge of, and comply with, the current syllabus requirements. Where candidates are entered for examinations by a teacher, the teacher must take responsibility that candidates are entered in accordance with the current syllabus requirements. Failure to carry out any of the examination requirements may lead to disqualification.
- For candidates with special needs, a letter giving details, and medical certificate as appropriate, should be attached.
- Any practical appointment requests (e.g. 'prefer morning,' or 'prefer weekdays') must be made at the time of entry. **LCM and its Representatives will take note of the information given, however, no guarantees can be made that all wishes will be met.**
- Submission of this entry is an undertaking to abide by the current regulations as listed in the current syllabus and any subsequent regulations updates published in the LCM Examinations Newsletter issued each term.
- Entries for public centres should be sent **to the LCM local representative**. Contact the LCM office for details of your nearest centre or to enquire about setting up your own centre.

Examination Fee   £ _____

Late Entry Fee (if necessary)   £ _____

Total amount submitted   £ _____
Cheques or postal orders should be made payable to **'Thames Valley University'**.

A current list of fees and entry deadlines is available from LCM Exams.

NON-UK ENTRIES

Visit the LCM Exams website
to find the local
exam representative
for your area:
http://mercury.tvu.ac.uk/lcmexams
(Note: the website address does not begin with www.)

The standard LCM music entry form is NOT valid for Classical Guitar entries. **Entry to the examination is only possible via this original form. Photocopies of this form will not be accepted under any circumstances.**

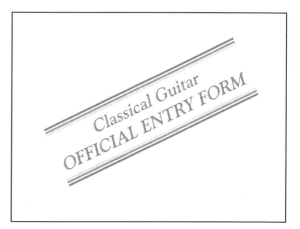